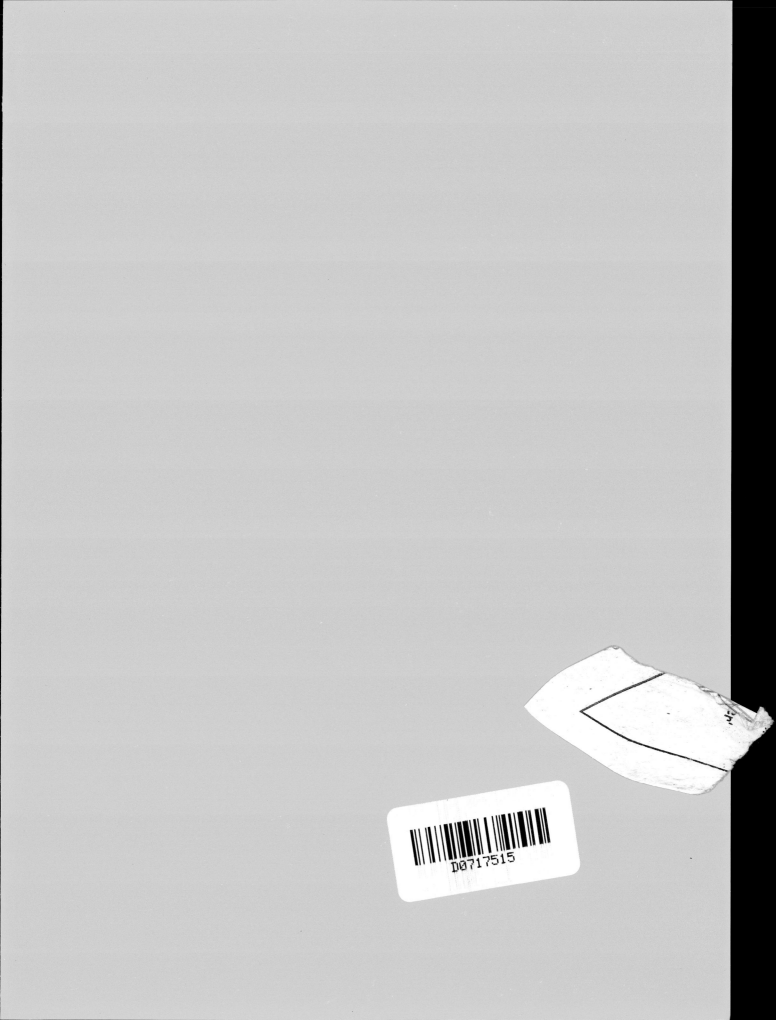

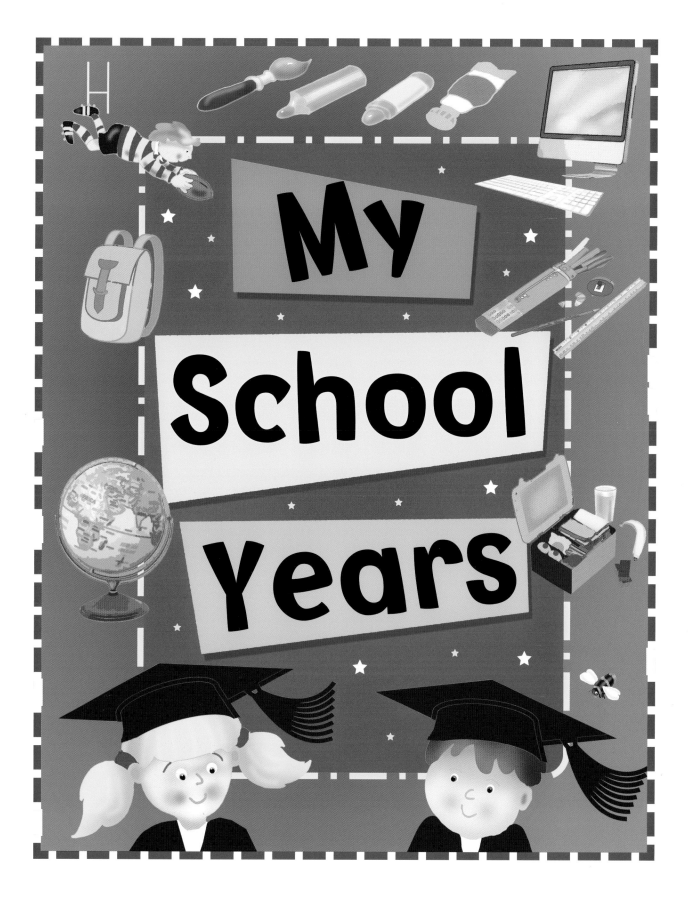

My School Years

Brown Watson

ENGLAND

Contents

My First Day at School............. 3

Reception Class..................... 4

Year One 8

Year Two 12

Year Three 16

Year Four........................... 20

Year Five 24

Year Six............................ 28

Year Seven 32

Year Eight.......................... 36

Year Nine........................... 40

Year Ten 44

Year Eleven......................... 46

Further Education.................. 48

First published 2011 by Brown Watson
The Old Mill, 76 Fleckney Road,
Kibworth Beauchamp, Leic LE8 0HG

ISBN: 978-0-7097-1915-1

My First Day at School

This is me on my
first day at school.

I went to my first real school on ....(date).

It is called ....

I was taken to school by ....

On my first day at school, I ....

....

....

....

Reception Class

Age:......... Height:.......... Weight:............

My teacher's name is ....

My favourite lesson is ....

My favourite game is ....

My favourite story is ....

I am good at ....

I am best friends with......................................

I went on school trips to ....

....

....

This is my
Reception Class
photograph

You can see me in the.......row,.......in from the.......

My classmates are..................................
....
....
....
....
....

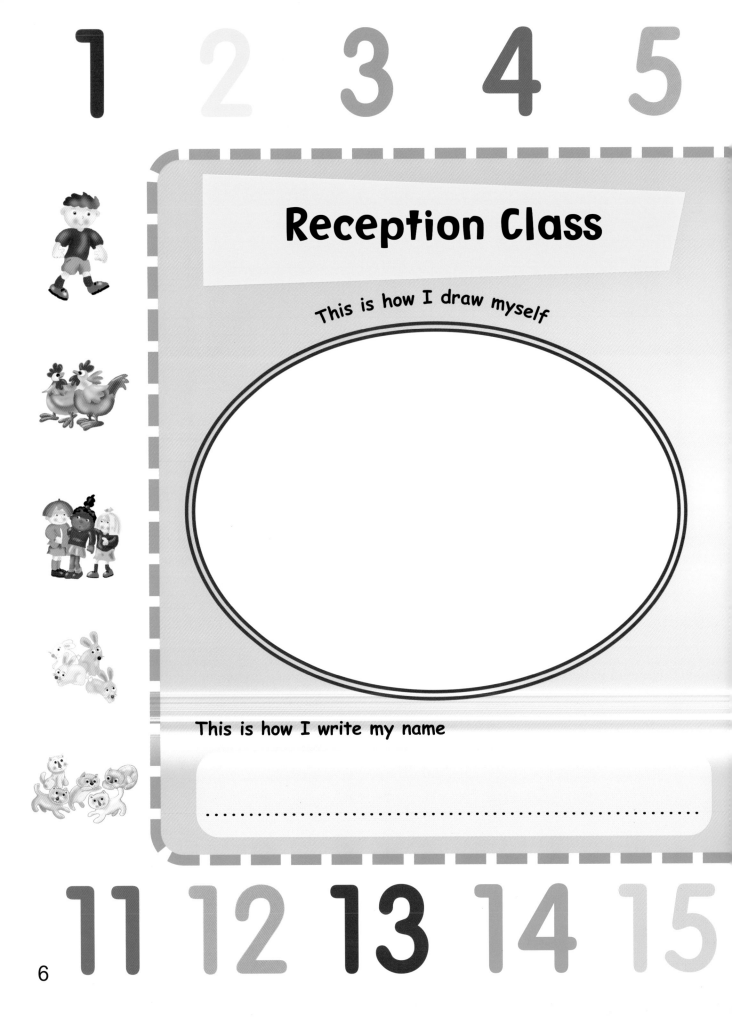

Reception Class

This is how I draw myself

This is how I write my name

....

I made this in Reception

Year One

Age:.......... Height:.......... Weight:..........

My teacher's name is..............................

My favourite lesson is..............................

My favourite game is ....

My favourite story is ....

I am good at..............................

I am best friends with..............................

I enjoyed the school trip to..............................

....

....

2 4 6 8 10

apple ball cat dog

**This is my
class photograph
from Year One**

You can see me in the.......row,.......in from the.......

My classmates are...................................
....
....
....
....
....

12

14

16

18

20

eag   fish   arapes   hat

Year One

This is how I draw myself

This is how I write my name

When I grow up, I want to be..........................

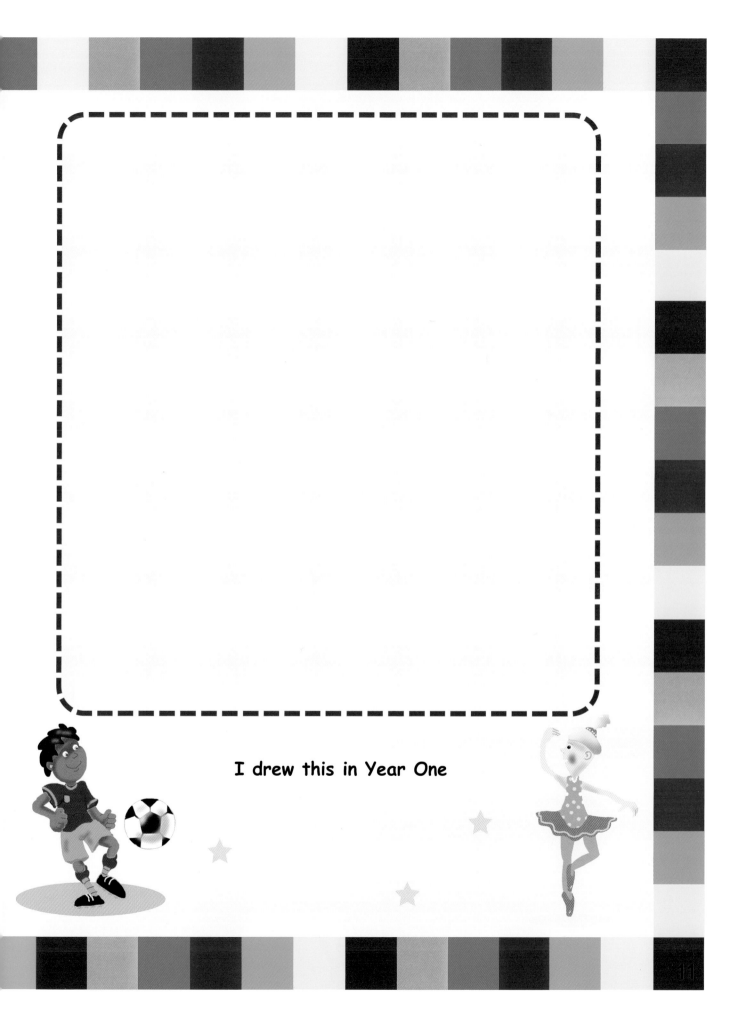

I drew this in Year One

Year Two

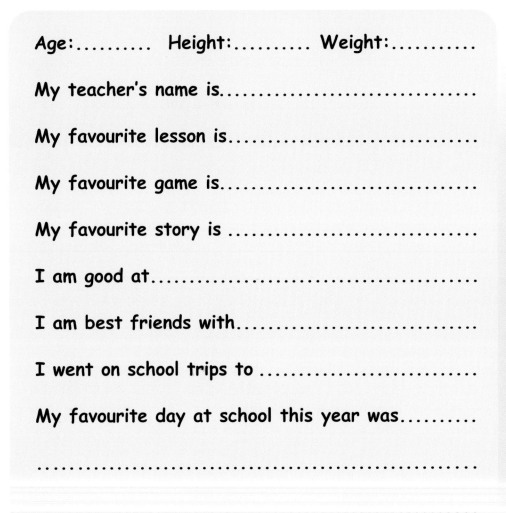

Age:.......... Height:.......... Weight:...........

My teacher's name is..............................

My favourite lesson is..............................

My favourite game is..............................

My favourite story is ....

I am good at..............................

I am best friends with..............................

I went on school trips to ....

My favourite day at school this year was..........

....

....

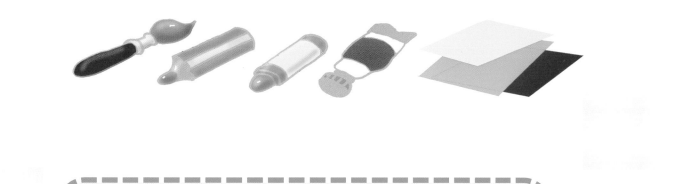

This is my
class photograph
from Year Two

You can see me in the.......row,.......in from the.......

My classmates are...................................
....
....
....
....
....
....

Year Two

This is how I draw myself

This is how I write my name

....

This year, I have learnt how to..................................

....

....

I made this in Year Two

15

Year Three

Age:.......... Height:.......... Weight:...........

My teacher's name is...............................

My favourite subject is...............................

My favourite game is...............................

My favourite book is...............................

I am good at...............................

I am best friends with...............................

I went on school trips to ....

The funniest day at school this year was when....

....

....

....

This is my
class photograph
from Year Three

You can see me in the........row,........in from the.......

My classmates are................................

....

....

....

....

....

Year Three

This is how I sign my name

....

This is my self-portrait

My favourite project this year was on . . . .

....

....

....

....

....

....

....

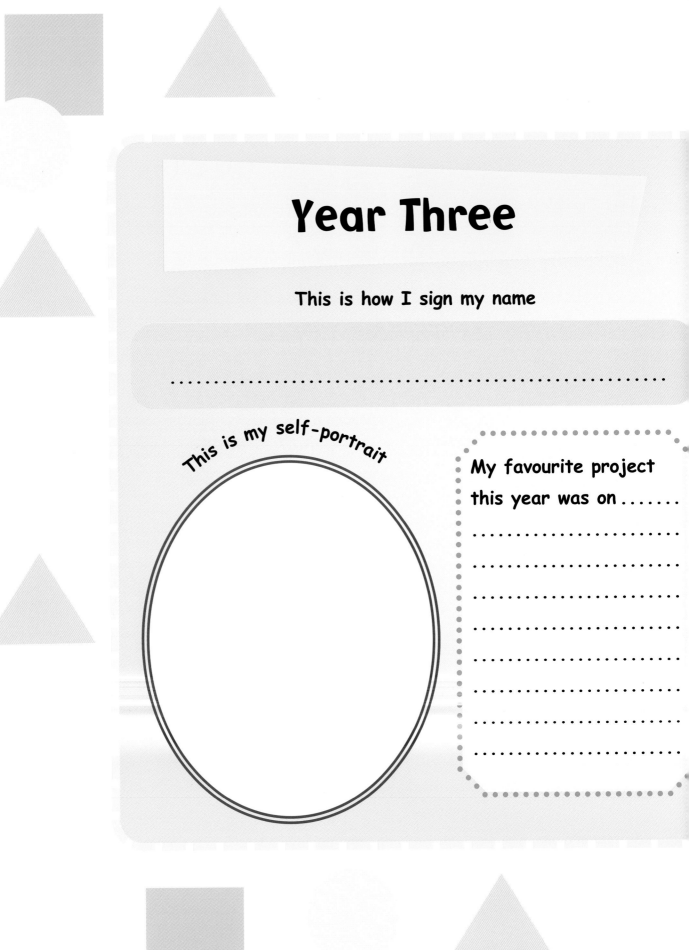

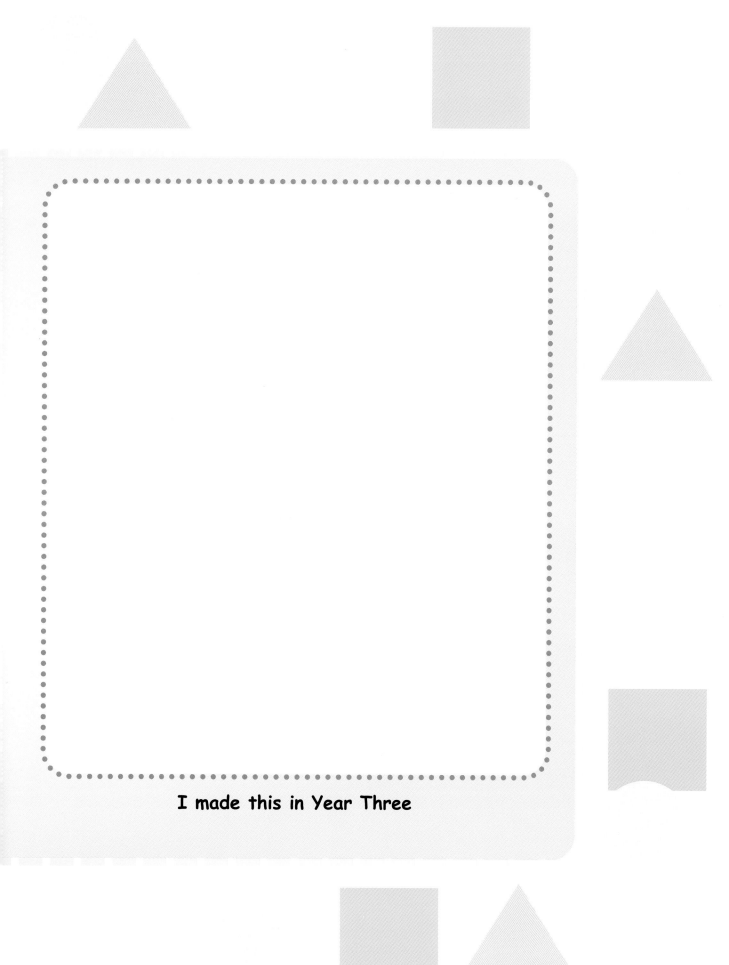

I made this in Year Three

Year Four

Age:......... Height:......... Weight:..........

My teacher's name is...............................

My favourite subject is.............................

My favourite sport is...............................

My favourite book is................................

I am good at..

I am best friends with..............................

I went on school trips to ....

My favourite activity in class this year was ....

....

....

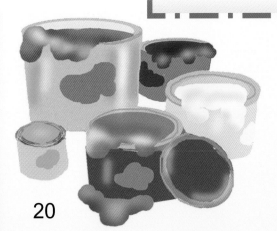

This is my
class photograph
from Year Four

You can see me in the.......row,.......in from the.......

My classmates are...
....
....
....
....
....
....

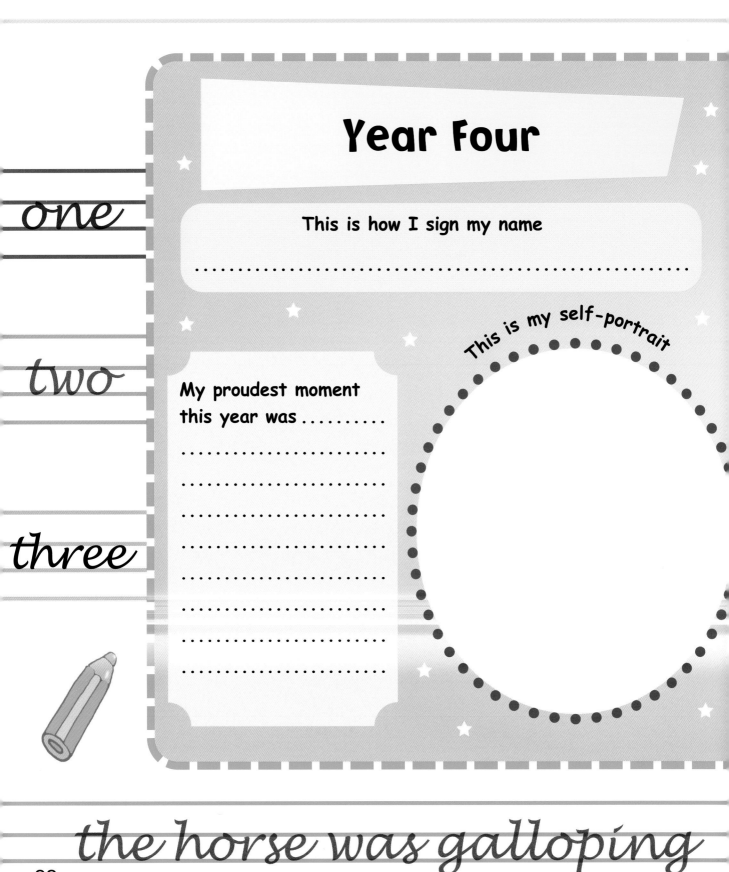

one

two

three

Year Four

This is how I sign my name

....

This is my self-portrait

My proudest moment
this year was ....

....
....
....
....
....
....
....

the horse was galloping

four

five

six

This is my favourite Year Four project

once upon a time

Year Five

Age:.......... Height:.......... Weight:...........

My teacher's name is ....

My favourite subject is...............................

My favourite sport is ....

My favourite book is ....

I am good at...

I am best friends with................................

I went on school trips to ....

I was really pleased to learn how to ....

....

....

**This is my
class photograph
from Year Five**

You can see me in the.......row,.......in from the.......

My classmates are.....................
....
....
....
....
....
....
....
....

Year Five

This is how I sign my name

....

When I grow up, I want to be ....

....

....

....

....

....

....

....

....

....

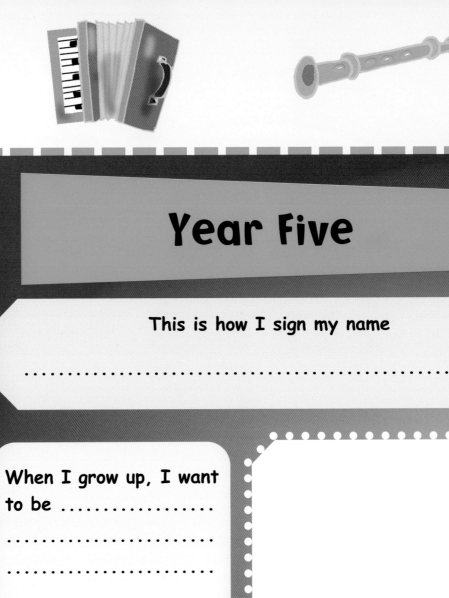

This is my self-portrait

26

This is my favourite Year Five project

Year Six

Age:......... Height:......... Weight:.........

My teacher's name is............................

My favourite lesson is............................

My favourite game is............................

My favourite story is............................

I am good at............................

I am best friends with............................

I went on school trips to ....

My greatest achievement this year was.........

....

....

**This is my
class photograph
from Year Six**

You can see me in the.......row,.......in from the.......

My classmates are...................................
....
....
....
....
....
....

Year Six

This is my
signature

....

My favourite project this
year was on ....
....
....
....
....

The funniest moment
this year was............
....
....
....
....
....
....
....
....

This is my self-portrait

Final Thoughts on Primary School

My favourite teachers were . . . .

. . . .

. . . .

My favourite subjects were . . . .

. . . .

. . . .

The most embarrassing moment was . . . .

. . . .

. . . .

My happiest memories are . . . .

. . . .

. . . .

My greatest achievement was. . . . .

. . . .

Year Seven

Age:......... Height:......... Weight:..........

Name of Secondary School........................

On my first day at Secondary School, I..........

....

....

Subjects ....

....

Teachers ....

....

....

Achievements ....

....

....

This is my
class photograph
from Year Seven

You can see me in the.......row,.......in from the.......

My classmates are...
....
....
....

Year Seven

Favourite assignments..

....

....

....

....

School trips ....

....

....

....

....

....

Interests................

....

....

....

....

....

School sporting events ....

....

....

....

Ambitions.......................

....

....

....

....

....

Best friends............

....

....

....

....

....

My signature...................................

Year Eight

Age:......... Height:.......... Weight:...........

Subjects..

....

....

....

Teachers...

....

....

Favourite subjects...

....

....

Favourite assignments...

....

....

This is my
class photograph
from Year Eight

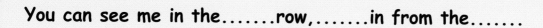

You can see me in the.......row,.......in from the.......

My classmates are ....
....
....
....
....
....
....
....
....
....
....

Year Eight

Achievements . . . .

. . . .

. . . .

School trips . . . .

. . . .

. . . .

. . . .

. . . .

School sporting events

. . . .

. . . .

. . . .

. . . .

. . . .

I admire...

....

....

Best friends...............

....

....

....

Interests.................

....

....

....

Memorable moments this year...............................

....

....

My signature...

Year Nine

Age:......... Height:.......... Weight:...........

Subjects...

....

....

....

Teachers..

....

....

Favourite subjects ....

....

....

Favourite assignments ....

....

....

This is my
class photograph
from Year Nine

You can see me in the.......row,.......in from the.......

My classmates are.................................
....
....
....
....
....
....

Year Nine

Achievements . . . .

. . . .

. . . .

School trips . . . .

. . . .

. . . .

. . . .

. . . .

. . . .

School sporting events

. . . .

. . . .

. . . .

. . . .

. . . .

Memorable school event this year . . . .

. . . .

I admire..

....

Best friends............

....

....

....

Interests................

....

....

....

Favourite moments this year.............................

....

Ambitions.................

....

....

....

My signature

Year Ten

Age:......... Height:......... Weight:..........

Subjects...

....

....

Teachers ....

....

....

Favourite subjects ....

....

Achievements ....

....

....

Best friends.....................................

Dreams and ambitions.............................

This is my
class photograph
from Year Ten

You can see me in the........row,........in from the.......

My classmates are.....................................
....
....
....
....
....

My signature....................................

Year Eleven

Age:.......... Height:.......... Weight:..........

Subjects...

....

....

Teachers ....

....

....

Examinations and achievements ....

....

....

....

Career goals / ambitions ....

Best friends...

Most memorable moment this year..................

....

$x + 4 = 9$
$x + 4 - 4 = 9 - 4$
$x + 0 = 5$
$x = 5$

$8x + 7y - 3x$
$= 8x - 3x + 7y$
$= 5x + 7y$

$6a - 3b - 4a - 4b + 3$
$= 6a - 4a - 3b - 4b + 3$
$= 2a - 7b + 3$

This is my
class photograph
from Year Eleven

You can see me in the.......row,.......in from the.......

My classmates are.....................................
....
....
....
....
....
....
....

My final thoughts on Secondary School

....
....
....
....

My signature

....

Further Education

Subjects..

....

....

Tutors..

....

....

Examinations and achievements..

....

....

....

My plans are now to

....

....

....

....

....

....

....